Angel

By Suzanne Siegel Zenkel

Design by Lesley Ehlers

PETER PAUPER PRESS, INC.
WHITE PLAINS, NEW YORK

Cover illustration from the private colllection of Ralph and Diane Hellebuyck, Old Print Factory, Inc.

Copyright © 1995
Peter Pauper Press, Inc.
202 Mamaroneck Avenue
White Plains, NY 10601
All rights reserved
ISBN 0-88088-595-5
Printed in China
7 6 5 4 3 2

CONTENTS

Introduction

Since the beginning of time, angels have been heralded as symbols of beauty and as the makers of miracles—delicate, winged creatures draped in filmy white, heaven-sent to deliver God's messages and to bring goodness through their special powers.

What makes angels so personal to each of us, though, is that their sole mission is to act on our behalf. Sharing their boundless wisdom, guardian angels take us under their wings. Selflessly, they help guide us to the places in our lives that bring us joy and peace of mind.

Angels appear and reappear in many shapes and guises. And for every person who has actually seen her angel, there are countless others who remain unaware that they have an angel who makes miracles happen for them. Though we're often unaware of our angel's presence, we can rest assured that our angel works diligently on our behalf every day and every night.

As you turn these pages, open your mind to the possibilities your secret angel presents. Reflect on the angel inspirations that follow. Be encouraged by the stories that illustrate what angels can do to make fairy tales come true for each of us. And always remember, all your angel needs is a warm place in your heart to make her feel at home.

 S. S. Z.

Embrace your
secret angel—
she's never more than an
arm's length away.

Moments of Joy

When a good person is troubled, an angel descends from heaven and embraces her. The angel carries the sorrow-filled person on her wings through the skies, pausing at places her passenger once loved.

First, she takes her passenger to a place well-remembered, where the perfume of spring flowers pervades a lush meadow.

From there, she carries her to the tip of a snow-capped mountain overlooking a crystal-clear lake, its serene surface reflecting a long-forgotten tranquility.

The angel's last stop is a playground, filled with the most beautiful music of all:

the sound of children's laughter.

The journey over, the once-
saddened passenger realizes
that her troubles have been replaced by
the scent, sight, and sounds of beauty and
happiness. She is shown that sorrow need
not be permanent—that she can always
hitch a ride on her angel's wings to
recapture moments of joy.

The music of angels
brings harmony where
there's discord.

In the roughest seas, your
angel will shelter you from
the storm.

Amid deafening noise, your angel will hear your softest whisper.

An angel's love is based only on what she knows of you in her mind and heart, never on how she beholds you with her eyes . . . an angel's love is blind.

Let your secret angel's wings lift you outside the realm of the ordinary.

The voice of an angel is in tune with the strings of your heart.

As you journey through
   your life,
Let your angel be your
   guide.
You'll discover secret places,
If you keep her by your
   side.

The Colors of the Rainbow

"Child," asked the Angel, "how do you feel about rainbows?"

"Rainbows!" said the Child scornfully, "how could I have a Rainbow with my dull life? You have to have sunshine for that!"

"Ah, but, Child," returned the Angel, "you also have to have rain. Do you know," she continued, "what the Rainbow-Colors mean?"

The Angel smoothed her long white wings. "Violet is for Other-People's Sorrows. Indigo is Troubles-of-Your-Own. True Blue is for Honest-Purposes, and Green for Happy-Memories."

"And Yellow?" said the Child softly. "I love yellow!"

"Yellow is the Blessings-We-Forget. Orange, splendid glowing Orange, is God's Promise-of-Victory, and Red is the Richness-of-Life-After-All."

The Angel bent to tighten her heel-wings. "So you see, Child, you need both Sun and Rain to make a Rainbow."

"I see," said the Child. "What is the Sun?"

"The Sun is the Love-That-is-in-You."

"Oh!" said the Child. "And what is the Rain?"

"The Rain is the Need-Right-Around-

You."

"Oh!" said the Child. "And is there a Rainbow for me to see?"

"Of course, my Child," said the Angel, smiling, "it's there for you always, just as I am."

Adapted from "The Colours of the Rainbow" by Gladys Wolcott Barnes (The Wonder Garden)

Just as you welcome your friends to your home and to your heart, welcome your angel to your self and to your soul.

Your angel is your steadfast companion—she lingers through dream-filled nights and busy days, and touches your actions with gentleness and warmth.

Open your heart. The angels will count you among their peace-loving, warm-hearted friends.

Treat your loved ones as your angel treats you—with compassion, respect, and generosity.

Your angel is always seated beside you, even when there's standing room only.

Angels always listen and understand. No matter what your native tongue, your angel speaks the same language.

I looked upon a star one
    night
And saw my angel's wings
    in flight.
And as she hovered over-
    head
I smiled and snuggled into
    bed.

The Golden Strawberries

Long ago, a poor woman lived in a little hut near a mountain on which was a wide forest. She had one daughter, and they loved each other dearly.

One day the woman fell ill, and longed for strawberries. So her daughter took a jug and set out to gather the fruit. She climbed the mountain, and entered the forest, where she found vines covered with big, red, luscious berries.

She had gathered her jug nearly full when she saw a tiny woman, who could barely walk, come tripping toward her. A very strange-looking woman she was; she appeared almost weightless, covered in a misty veil of gauze. When she spoke, she sang in melodies sweeter than the young woman had ever heard.

"My dear child," said she, "I see that your jug is full of delicious berries. Would you please give me some to quench my thirst?"

"Take all you want," said the young woman gladly, "and I'll pick more for my mother."

So the strange woman ate until the jug was nearly empty, then away she hobbled, vanishing among the trees.

The daughter quickly filled her jug again, and went home. Astonishingly, when she took it to her mother's bedside, every strawberry in it had turned to pure gold! Mother and daughter hugged each other joyfully, thanking the heavens for their bounty.

And from that day on mother and daughter were very rich indeed.

Sometimes you know an angel only by the miracles she bestows upon your doorstep.

Let your spirit burst forth like the sun's rays and bask in the glow of your angel's benevolence.

No matter what may be in vogue, an angel's devotion never goes out of style.

Reach for the heavens and discover your secret angel.

Let your angel take you under her wing.

With an angel by your side, you'll never be afraid of your own shadow.

Your angel's love is 100% recyclable—it reappears in many forms.

The first star I gaze upon
   tonight
Will be my angel's guiding
   light.
Amid all joy and hope or
   fear,
My angel hovers ever near.

The Angel's Gift

There lives an Angel so gentle and charming that all who meet her want to remain in her midst. The time comes, though, when each person has to go out into the world, and when that time comes the Angel gives to each whatever gift is asked of her. It is chiefly the story of Tessa that you will hear now.

The Angel loved Tessa with all her heart, and Tessa had nearly reached the age at which the gifts are generally bestowed. However, the Angel wanted Tessa to consider her gift carefully beforehand. So the Angel decided to send her to see three women whose wishes had already been granted.

Upon Tessa's return from her first trip, the

Angel said, "Now Tessa, tell me what impression you have received." "You sent me," answered Tessa, "to the home of Amanda, on whom you had bestowed the gift of beauty. It seemed to me that her loveliness, which fairly dazzled me at first, had absolutely deprived her of the use of any of her other gifts or graces. In allowing herself to be seen, she appeared to think that she was doing all that could possibly be required of her. But unfortunately, while I was still with her she became seriously ill, and although she soon recovered, her beauty is entirely gone, so that she hates the very sight of herself and is in despair."

Some time passed, and the Angel sent for Tessa again, and told her she was going to stay for a while with Claudia. But she was there only a very little time before returning. "Ah," Tessa cried, "what a place you sent me to that time!" "Why, what was the matter?" asked the Angel. "Claudia had asked for the gift of eloquence, if I remember rightly." "And very ill the gift of eloquence becomes a person," replied Tessa, "when she never leaves off talking. It is true that she speaks well, and her expressions are well chosen, but she talks endlessly without fear of interruption. Oh! How glad I was to come away, I cannot tell you."

After allowing Tessa a little time to recover, the Angel sent her to see Olivia, to whom she had given the gift of pleasing others. When Tessa returned, she said to the Angel, "I thought, at first, that Olivia must be the happiest woman in the world; she had a thousand friends and lovers who vied with one another for her attention.

Indeed, I had nearly decided that I would ask for a similar gift." "Have you changed your mind, then?" asked the Angel. "Yes, indeed, Angel," replied Tessa, "and I will tell you why. The longer I stayed the more I saw that Olivia was not really happy. In her desire to please everyone she ceased to be sincere, and even her friends felt that the charms that were exercised upon all who approached her without distinction were valueless, so that in the end they ceased to care for her, and went away disdainfully."

The Angel agreed in her heart with Tessa's conclusions. Now the time had come for Tessa to receive her gift. The Angel stood in the midst and in the usual manner asked what she would take with her into the great world.

Tessa paused for a moment, and then answered: "The comfort to be myself." And the Angel granted her request.

For the Angel knew that Tessa already possessed two of life's most prized gifts: Goodness, and the Wisdom to appreciate that and use it thoughtfully. All three of these treasured gifts bring happiness to their possessors, and all who are brought into contact with them.

Adapted from "Fairy Gifts"
by the Comte de Caylus
(The Green Fairy Book)

Offering of affection with loving wishes.

The only time an angel weeps is when her song falls on deaf ears.

Your angel's touch can be felt in a warm summer breeze, her music heard in the melody of a songbird, and her beauty seen in a rainbow sunset . . . Your angel is always near.

Whether you're waiting in the wings or taking center stage, your angel's always behind the scenes.

No matter what your sense of direction, you'll never lose your way. Your angel will always keep you on the right path.

In the marathon of life,
your angel will push you
to go the extra mile.

Your angel is the mirror
of your soul—if you look,
you will always find her
reflected within.

Angels may not dress
the part,
With robes and wings
that soar.
Often angels come as
friends
Knocking at your door.

How the Rose Got Its Fragrance

There is an enchanting wonder tale, telling how, on a lovely Spring day, the Angel of the Flowers lay down to rest beneath a blushing Rose Bush. All throughout the evening she had been sprinkling the flowers and grass with dew, and she had grown tired. She rested her weary head among the Roses, and slept. When she awoke, she said: "Most beautiful of all my flowers, I thank you for your refreshing shade and extraordinary beauty. If you could only speak, and ask me for a favor, how gladly I would grant it." The Rose Bush quickly replied, "Adorn me with a new charm, if you would be so kind."

So the Angel adorned the Roses with the

sweetest, most delicate scent in all the land, and said: "May all who dwell around this glorious Rose Bush savor its delightful fragrance evermore."

Always save a place in
your heart rent-free so your
angel will often come to
stay with you.

Call your angel any time—
you'll never be put on hold.

You'll navigate life's rough seas better with an angel as your first mate.

Where there is goodness, there is an angel.

The fruits borne by your guardian angel are always in season.

Listen for your angel's voice in music, in kind words, and in loving thoughts.

On any path that you
may stroll,
Keep your angel in your
soul.

How the First Snowdrop Came

As Eve sat weeping for lost Paradise, and as she mourned for the many beautiful flowers that had grown in the Garden, an Angel flew down to Earth to comfort her.

Now, since the Fall, no green thing had sprung up, but everywhere lay the thick white Snow, and the whole World was cold and bleak.

The Angel caught a passing Snowflake, and gently breathed upon it. It fell to Earth, and, lo! it was a flake no more, but a folded bud, white and deliciously fragrant.

"This bud," said the Angel, "is a promise

∽ 49 ∾

that Summer shall come again, and bring fruits and flowers to gladden the hearts of all."

The Angel's mission done, away she flew.

And, lo! where last her wings have swept the Snows,
A quaintly fashioned ring of milk-white Snowdrops blows!

Your guardian angel asks
for nothing in return;
her only reward is your
happiness.

Your angel has no office
hours—her door is always
open.

Let your angel tend the garden of your soul, and your path will be strewn with roses.

On those gloomy days, hitch a ride on your secret angel's wings. You'll be lifted high above the clouds.

Give to your secret angel
what she has bestowed upon
you: smiles and laughter,
charm, honesty, and
integrity.

Allow yourself to live as
your angel lives—in
serenity, in love, and in
understanding.

May your life be a garden,
Ever green and ever thriving,
With your angel sowing
love,
And for goodness ever
striving.

The Angel and the Child

A wonderful little girl lived virtually alone. She had neither brother nor sister, nor friends who lived near her.

The little girl was blessed with a keen imagination, providing her with the companionship of playmates she really did not have. To her, the bushes and the trees were filled with other children, with whom she talked and played.

One afternoon, a strange winged woman came and asked her what game she was playing. The little girl, ruffled by the unexpected appearance of a stranger, gave only a whisper of a reply. But the woman smiled very kindly upon her.

"Tell me, dear Child," the woman said, "were you not imagining your yard filled with friends playing merrily until the sun sets?"

"Yes."

"And would it be your wish to have such friends as your neighbors?"

The little girl gazed up in awe and nodded. Thereupon the woman floated about the garden, touching each bush and tree, beckoning child after child to come forth and play. Soon the garden was filled with children playing gleefully, and the little girl was happier than she had ever dreamt. The strange winged woman remained until the sun set, and then she went away.

Every day, from then on, the little girl and her large circle of friends gathered to play in her yard until the sun set. And every night before turning in to bed, she imagined having the most delightful conversations with that strange winged woman who had magically filled her life with joy.

The once lonely girl never knew that the strange winged woman was her very own Guardian Angel. Little did she know that, day and night, her Angel hovered about her, invisible, but always watching out for her well-being.

Heaven and Earth, as it were, meet each other, and happily, good spirits sometimes walk the Earth.

When your vision is obscured, your angel will help you find a clear picture.

With an angel as part of the landscape, you'll always have a place in the sun.

On the road of life, let your angel be a backseat driver.

Be ready for your secret angel to transport you to the magical realm of realized dreams.

Rest assured that when you're sleeping, your angel is hard at work. She'll prove that even your wildest dreams can come true.

Your angel's touch is everywhere—in blooming flowers, sparkling streams, and star-filled skies.

An angel may seem
delicate,
As though she'd break in
two,
But she is stronger than
she looks,
And always there for you.